This Journal Belongs to

Healing

/ˈhiːlɪŋ/

Noun

1. the process of making or becoming sound or healthy again.
2. "the gift of healing"

Adjective

1. tending to heal; therapeutic.
2. "a healing experience"

Healing Journal for Black Men

The 5 Stages of
Healing

Stage 1: Denial

Stage 2: Anger

Stage 3: Depression

Stage 4: Acceptance/Getting Help

Stage 5: Recovery/Rehab

Your Grief Triggers

Grief Triggers	How are you handling it?

NOTES

It's okay

to begin your story today.
Those mistakes you've made
along the way are lessons,
not failures. You were meant
to get up and find a way that
resonates with you.
There is no expiration date
to reinventing yourself

Daily Check-in   Date:_____

You doing ok Bruh?

My Mood

:)	:(	>:(	:O	:')	^_^	:'(	?:(
Happy	Sad	Angry	Surprised	Anxious	Calm	Depressed	Confused

Let it Out

Why do you feel this way?

Self-Care Schedule

Daily Inspiration

I am one with all of life

How did you feel today?

Daily Check-in

Date:_____

You doing ok Bruh?

My Mood

| Happy | Sad | Angry | Surprised | Anxious | Calm | Depressed | Confused |

Let it Out

Why do you feel this way?

Self-Care Schedule

Daily Inspiration

I live an authentic life

If I weren't afraid, I would....

Daily Check-in

Date:_____

You doing ok Bruh?

My Mood

| Happy | Sad | Angry | Surprised | Anxious | Calm | Depressed | Confused |

Let it Out

Why do you feel this way?

Self-Care Schedule

Daily Inspiration

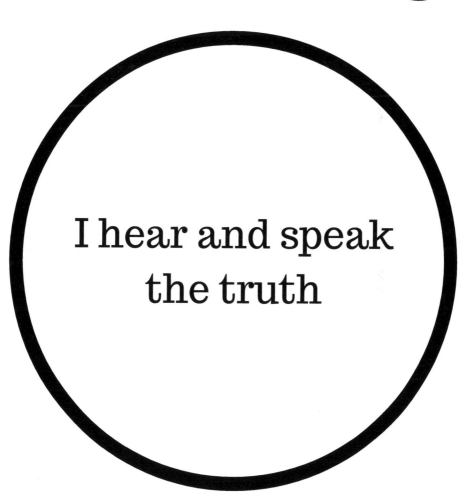

I hear and speak
the truth

It's important that I work on myself because....

Daily Check-in

Date:_____

You doing ok Bruh?

My Mood

Happy	Sad	Angry	Surprised	Anxious	Calm	Depressed	Confused

Let it Out

Why do you feel this way?

Self-Care Schedule

Daily Inspiration

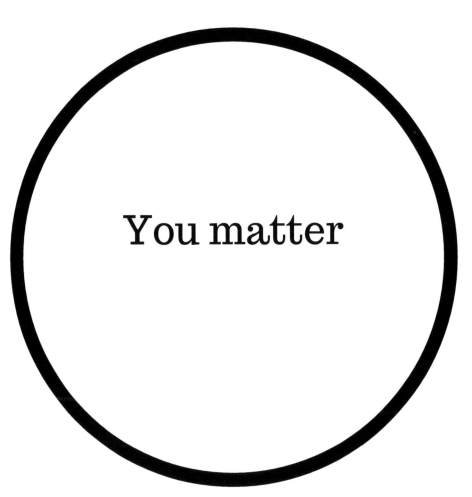

You matter

What are the top 3 things you value about yourself?

Daily Check-in   Date:_____

You doing ok Bruh?

My Mood

| Happy | Sad | Angry | Surprised | Anxious | Calm | Depressed | Confused |

Let it Out

Why do you feel this way?

Self-Care Schedule

Daily Inspiration

It is safe for you to give and receive love

Write a letter to the person who hurt you the most

Daily Check-in

Date:_____

You doing ok Bruh?

My Mood

| Happy | Sad | Angry | Surprised | Anxious | Calm | Depressed | Confused |

Let it Out

Why do you feel this way?

Self-Care Schedule

Daily Inspiration

I am the creator of my own universe

Write a letter of forgiveness to your younger self

Weekly Check-in

Monday

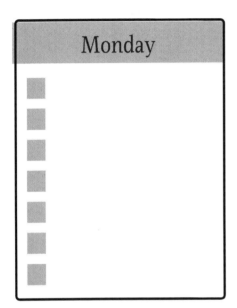

Tuesday

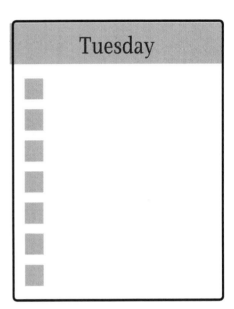

Wednesday

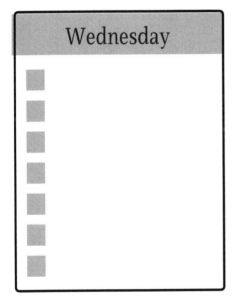

Thursday

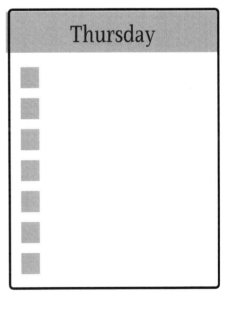

Weekly Check-in

Friday

Saturday

Sunday

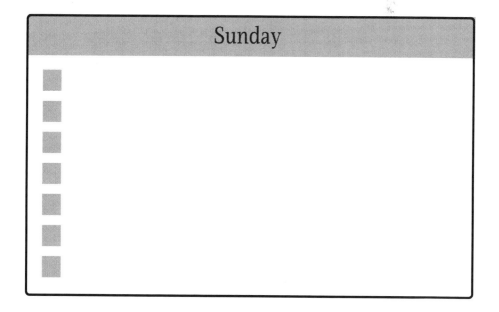

Daily Check-in   Date:_____

You doing ok Bruh?

My Mood

:)	:(	>:(	:O	:'(	:)	:'(	?:(
Happy	Sad	Angry	Surprised	Anxious	Calm	Depressed	Confused

Let it Out

Why do you feel this way?

Self-Care Schedule

Daily Inspiration

I live an authentic life

What is the biggest life you've ever told yourself?

Daily Check-in

Date:_____

You doing ok Bruh?

My Mood

| Happy | Sad | Angry | Surprised | Anxious | Calm | Depressed | Confused |

Let it Out

Why do you feel this way?

Self-Care Schedule

Daily Inspiration

I act with courage and strenght

What are the top three things you want to change in your relationship with your parents?

Daily Check-in

Date:_____

You doing ok Bruh?

My Mood

| Happy | Sad | Angry | Surprised | Anxious | Calm | Depressed | Confused |

Let it Out

Why do you feel this way?

Self-Care Schedule

Daily Inspiration

I am a sensual and creative being

What are the top three things you want to change in your relationship with yourself?

Daily Check-in

Date:_____

You doing ok Bruh?

My Mood

| Happy | Sad | Angry | Surprised | Anxious | Calm | Depressed | Confused |

Let it Out

Why do you feel this way?

Self-Care Schedule

Daily Inspiration

I trust more and I fear less

What are the top three things you want to change in your relationship with your friends?

Daily Check-in

Date:_____

You doing ok Bruh?

My Mood

Happy	Sad	Angry	Surprised	Anxious	Calm	Depressed	Confused

Let it Out

Why do you feel this way?

Self-Care Schedule

Daily Inspiration

I am confident in
what I do

What are the top three things you want to change in your relationship with your colleagues?

Daily Check-in

Date:_____

You doing ok Bruh?

My Mood

| Happy | Sad | Angry | Surprised | Anxious | Calm | Depressed | Confused |

Let it Out

Why do you feel this way?

Self-Care Schedule

Daily Inspiration

I trust myself to make the right decisions

How are you spending your spare time?

Daily Check-in   Date:_____

You doing ok Bruh?

My Mood

| Happy | Sad | Angry | Surprised | Anxious | Calm | Depressed | Confused |

Let it Out

Why do you feel this way?

Self-Care Schedule

Daily Inspiration

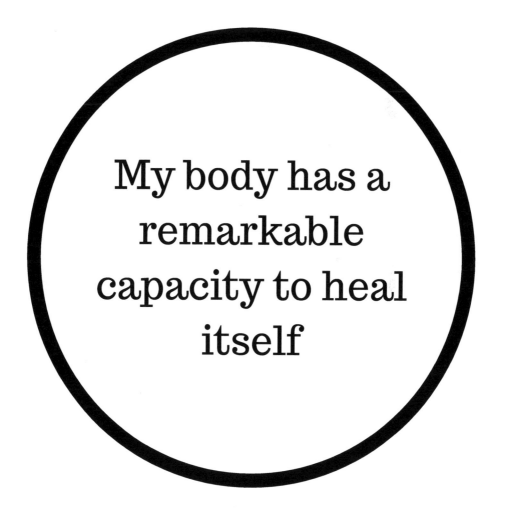

My body has a
remarkable
capacity to heal
itself

How did you feel about the trauma you experienced?

Weekly Check-in

Monday
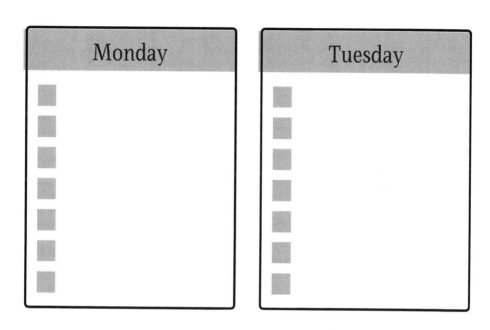

Tuesday

Wednesday
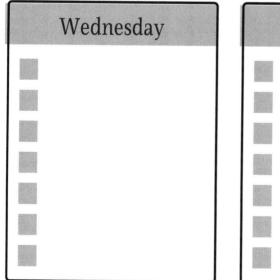

Thursday

Weekly Check-in

Friday

Saturday

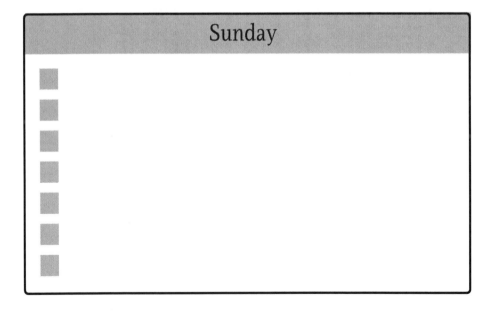

Sunday

Daily Check-in

Date:_____

You doing ok Bruh?

My Mood

Happy	Sad	Angry	Surprised	Anxious	Calm	Depressed	Confused

Let it Out

Why do you feel this way?

Self-Care Schedule

Daily Inspiration

My healing is
already in process

During tough times, what helps you the most and why?

Daily Check-in

Date:_____

You doing ok Bruh?

My Mood

| Happy | Sad | Angry | Surprised | Anxious | Calm | Depressed | Confused |

Let it Out

Why do you feel this way?

Self-Care Schedule

Daily Inspiration

I am grateful for
my perfect health

List 5 ways you practice self-care

Daily Check-in   Date:_____

You doing ok Bruh?

My Mood

| Happy | Sad | Angry | Surprised | Anxious | Calm | Depressed | Confused |

Let it Out

Why do you feel this way?

Self-Care Schedule

Daily Inspiration

I am worthy of a
great life

How would your life be like, without the trauma you experienced?

Daily Check-in

Date:_____

You doing ok Bruh?

My Mood

☺	☹	😠	😮	😰	😌	😢	❓
Happy	Sad	Angry	Surprised	Anxious	Calm	Depressed	Confused

Let it Out

Why do you feel this way?

Self-Care Schedule

Daily Inspiration

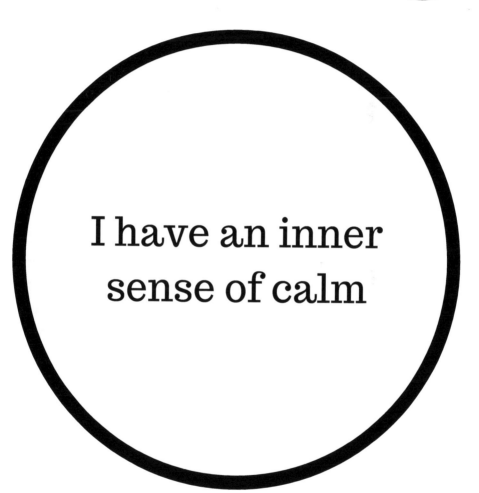

I have an inner
sense of calm

What are some things you would like to hear from someone

Daily Check-in   Date:_____

You doing ok Bruh?

My Mood

| Happy | Sad | Angry | Surprised | Anxious | Calm | Depressed | Confused |

Let it Out

Why do you feel this way?

Self-Care Schedule

Daily Inspiration

I will do what I
love to do

What are three core things you can do for yourself?

Daily Check-in

Date:_____

You doing ok Bruh?

My Mood

| Happy | Sad | Angry | Surprised | Anxious | Calm | Depressed | Confused |

Let it Out

Why do you feel this way?

Self-Care Schedule

Daily Inspiration

I am unaffected by the judgement of others

Why are you putting yourself last?

Daily Check-in   Date:_____

You doing ok Bruh?

My Mood

| Happy | Sad | Angry | Surprised | Anxious | Calm | Depressed | Confused |

Let it Out

Why do you feel this way?

Self-Care Schedule

Daily Inspiration

Loving myself works miracles in my life

What are you tolerating that you do not want?

Daily Check-in

Date:_____

You doing ok Bruh?

My Mood

| Happy | Sad | Angry | Surprised | Anxious | Calm | Depressed | Confused |

Let it Out

Why do you feel this way?

Self-Care Schedule

Daily Inspiration

I am worthy and
true to myself

What are some things you would do to change your life for the better?

Weekly Check-in

Monday

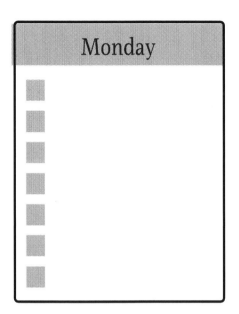

Tuesday

Wednesday

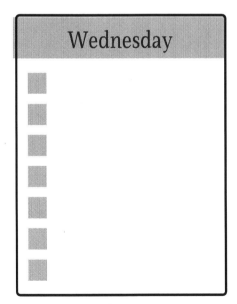

Thursday

Weekly Check-in

Friday

Saturday

Sunday

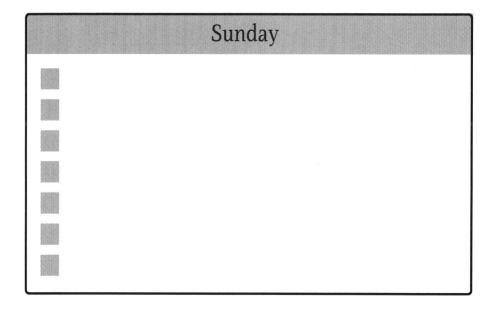

The Healing Path

Self-Healing Exercises

Here are a few exercises, that span the course of 7 days, to help you become more in touch with yourself, and your body. Prioritize each exercise for the given days, and see a change in your body, mind, and spirit in such a short amount of time.

Self-Healing Exercises

1. Breathing Exercises
2. Drink more water
3. Exercise for at least 10 minutes
4. Relax and let your mind go free
5. Meditation for at least 3 minutes
6. Close your eyes and don't let yourself be distracted
7. Go out and be in touch with nature

DAY 1
BREATHE

How did you feel after it?

DAY 2
WATER

How did you feel after it?

DAY 3
EXERCISE

How did you feel after it?

DAY 4
RELAX

How did you feel after it?

DAY 5
MEDITATION

How did you feel after it?

DAY 6
CLOSE YOUR EYES

How did you feel after it?

DAY 7
NATURE

How did you feel after it?

Habit Tracker

Habit Tracker

NOTES

NOTES

NOTES

NOTES

NOTES

NOTES

NOTES

NOTES

NOTES

NOTES

NOTES

NOTES

NOTES

Stress Relief

Release the stress you have inside of you to improve overall healing.

What makes you feel stressed?

What stresses you out the most?

What is within yor control and what isn't?

Can you improve this situation by changing your strategy towards it?

Will anything change if you worry a lot?

What helps you calm down?

Therapy Notes

Topic	Date	Other

Important

Therapy Notes

Therapy Notes

Topic	Date	Other

Important

Therapy Notes

Therapy Notes

Topic	Date	Other

Important

Therapy Notes

Days for Yoga

Days for Yoga

Mood Tracker

Happy	Sad	Normal
Angry	Curious	Grumpy
Excited	Sick	Energetic

Gratitude Log

What are you grateful for?

Gratitude Log

What are you grateful for?

Gratitude Log

What are you grateful for?

NOTES